# Juneteenth Paper Dolls

Paper doll set includes:

- Instructions
- A description of Juneteenth
- Two Paper Dolls
- Five dresses for each of your paper dolls
- Attached stand
- Envelope to store your paper dolls and their clothes

Artwork by Nova Edwards

e-mail:lvkpaperdolls@aol.com
www.lvkpaperdolls.etsy.com

## INSTRUCTIONS

The following instructions are provided to assist you with the enjoyment of your Juneteenth Paper Dolls:

- You will need the following items:
  - scissors
  - glue or tape
- Once your paper dolls and their clothes are cut out, use the tabs on the clothes to secure the dresses to the paper dolls.
- Fold the stand that is attached to the base of each doll on the dotted lines.
- Your paper dolls have an envelope in which you can place them and their clothes. To assemble the envelope, follow the instructions below:

  1. Remove the "Back of Envelope" page from the book by cutting on the heavy dashed line.
  2. Front of the envelope:
     a. Remove the front of the envelope (the page with the paper dolls' picture) from the book by cutting on the long, heavy dashed line
     b. Next, cut on the remaining heavy dashed lines
     c. With the front of the page facing you, fold on the dotted lines away from you (backwards) to create flaps
     d. Place the front of the envelope face down
  3. Take the back of the envelope and place it on top of the front of the envelope
  4. Tape or glue the flaps from the front of the envelope to the back of the envelope
  5. Now you're ready to place your paper dolls and their clothes in the envelope you created!

Please note, if you used glue, ***wait until the glue dries*** before placing your paper dolls and clothes in the envelope.

# Juneteenth: A Celebration of Freedom

Juneteenth, a combination of the words June and nineteenth, celebrates the end of slavery in the United States. On June 19, 1865, two and a half years after President Abraham Lincoln's official January 1, 1863, Emancipation Proclamation, Major-General Gordon Granger arrived in Texas with the news that the Civil War had ended and that the slaves were free. Prior to Major-General Granger's arrival, many of the slaves in the south did not know that they had been freed. Juneteenth is an important event to remember and celebrate because it commemorates the beginning of liberty and the end of the brutal, demeaning system under which people were forced to do hard labor without pay and were denied basic human rights.

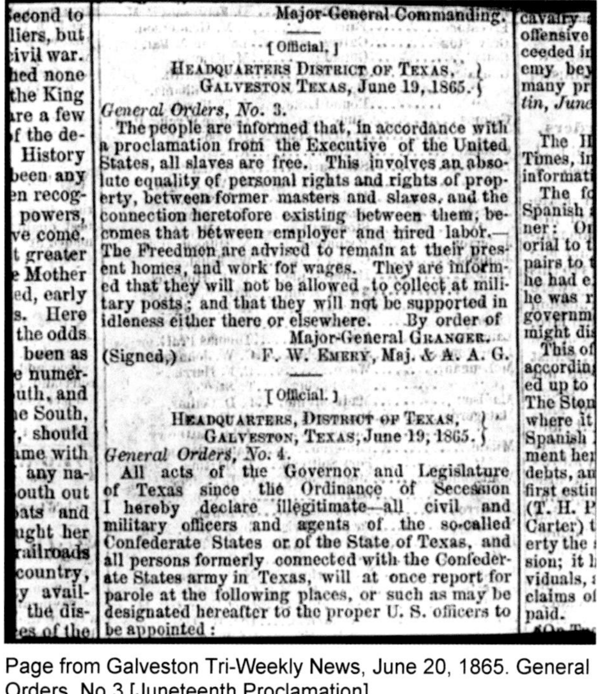

Major-General Commanding.

[Official.]

HEADQUARTERS DISTRICT OF TEXAS,
GALVESTON TEXAS, June 19, 1865.

*General Orders, No. 3.*

The people are informed that, in accordance with a proclamation from the Executive of the United States, all slaves are free. This involves an absolute equality of personal rights and rights of property, between former masters and slaves, and the connection heretofore existing between them, becomes that between employer and hired labor.—The Freedmen are advised to remain at their present homes, and work for wages. They are informed that they will not be allowed to collect at military posts; and that they will not be supported in idleness either there or elsewhere. By order of Major-General GRANGER.

(Signed,) F. W. EMERY, Maj. & A. A. G.

[Official.]

HEADQUARTERS, DISTRICT OF TEXAS,
GALVESTON, TEXAS, June 19, 1865.

*General Orders, No. 4.*

All acts of the Governor and Legislature of Texas since the Ordinance of Secession I hereby declare illegitimate—all civil and military officers and agents of the so-called Confederate States or of the State of Texas, and all persons formerly connected with the Confederate States army in Texas, will at once report for parole at the following places, or such as may be designated hereafter to the proper U. S. officers to be appointed:

Page from Galveston Tri-Weekly News, June 20, 1865. General Orders, No.3 [Juneteenth Proclamation].

Source: http://www.cah.utexas.edu/db/dmr/image_lg.php?variable=di_01803

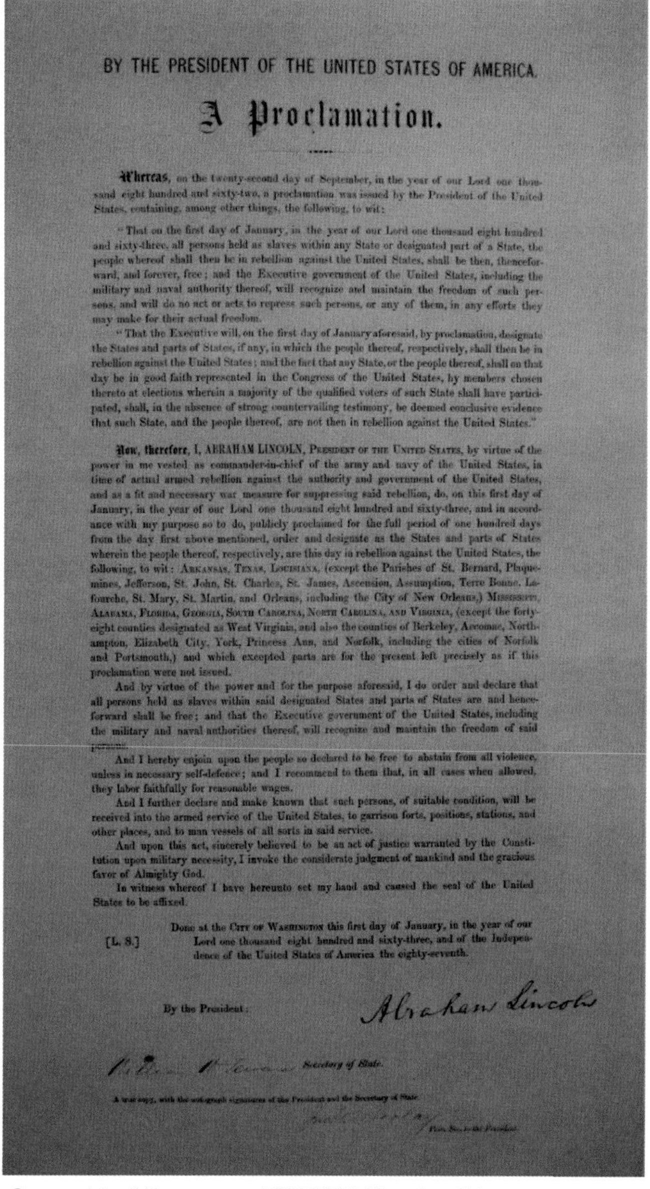

BY THE PRESIDENT OF THE UNITED STATES OF AMERICA.

A Proclamation.

Whereas, on the twenty-second day of September, in the year of our Lord one thousand eight hundred and sixty-two, a proclamation was issued by the President of the United States, containing, among other things, the following, to wit:

"That on the first day of January, in the year of our Lord one thousand eight hundred and sixty-three, all persons held as slaves within any State or designated part of a State, the people whereof shall then be in rebellion against the United States, shall be then, thenceforward, and forever, free; and the Executive government of the United States, including the military and naval authority thereof, will recognize and maintain the freedom of such persons, and will do no act or acts to repress such persons, or any of them, in any efforts they may make for their actual freedom.

"That the Executive will, on the first day of January aforesaid, by proclamation, designate the States and parts of States, if any, in which the people thereof, respectively, shall then be in rebellion against the United States; and the fact that any State, or the people thereof, shall on that day be in good faith represented in the Congress of the United States, by members chosen thereto at elections wherein a majority of the qualified voters of such State shall have participated, shall, in the absence of strong countervailing testimony, be deemed conclusive evidence that such State, and the people thereof, are not then in rebellion against the United States."

Now, therefore, I, ABRAHAM LINCOLN, PRESIDENT OF THE UNITED STATES, by virtue of the power in me vested as commander-in-chief of the army and navy of the United States, in time of actual armed rebellion against the authority and government of the United States, and as a fit and necessary war measure for suppressing said rebellion, do, on this first day of January, in the year of our Lord one thousand eight hundred and sixty-three, and in accordance with my purpose so to do, publicly proclaimed for the full period of one hundred days from the day first above mentioned, order and designate as the States and parts of States wherein the people thereof, respectively, are this day in rebellion against the United States, the following, to wit: ARKANSAS, TEXAS, LOUISIANA, (except the Parishes of St. Bernard, Plaquemines, Jefferson, St. John, St. Charles, St. James, Ascension, Assumption, Terre Bonne, Lafourche, St. Mary, St. Martin, and Orleans, including the City of New Orleans,) MISSISSIPPI, ALABAMA, FLORIDA, GEORGIA, SOUTH CAROLINA, NORTH CAROLINA, AND VIRGINIA, (except the forty-eight counties designated as West Virginia, and also the counties of Berkeley, Accomac, Northampton, Elizabeth City, York, Princess Ann, and Norfolk, including the cities of Norfolk and Portsmouth,) and which excepted parts are for the present left precisely as if this proclamation were not issued.

And by virtue of the power and for the purpose aforesaid, I do order and declare that all persons held as slaves within said designated States and parts of States are and henceforward shall be free; and that the Executive government of the United States, including the military and naval authorities thereof, will recognize and maintain the freedom of said persons.

And I hereby enjoin upon the people so declared to be free to abstain from all violence, unless in necessary self-defence; and I recommend to them that, in all cases when allowed, they labor faithfully for reasonable wages.

And I further declare and make known that such persons, of suitable condition, will be received into the armed service of the United States, to garrison forts, positions, stations, and other places, and to man vessels of all sorts in said service.

And upon this act, sincerely believed to be an act of justice warranted by the Constitution upon military necessity, I invoke the considerate judgment of mankind and the gracious favor of Almighty God.

In witness whereof I have hereunto set my hand and caused the seal of the United States to be affixed.

[L. S.] Done at the CITY OF WASHINGTON this first day of January, in the year of our Lord one thousand eight hundred and sixty-three, and of the Independence of the United States of America the eighty-seventh.

By the President: Abraham Lincoln

Secretary of State.

Source: http://dilemma-x.net/2012/06/19/juneteenth/

More information about Juneteenth:

- http://www.juneteenth.com/history.htm
- http://sacramentojuneteenthinc.org/history-of-juneteenth/
- "Juneteenth: A Celebration of Freedom," by Dr. Charles A. Taylor

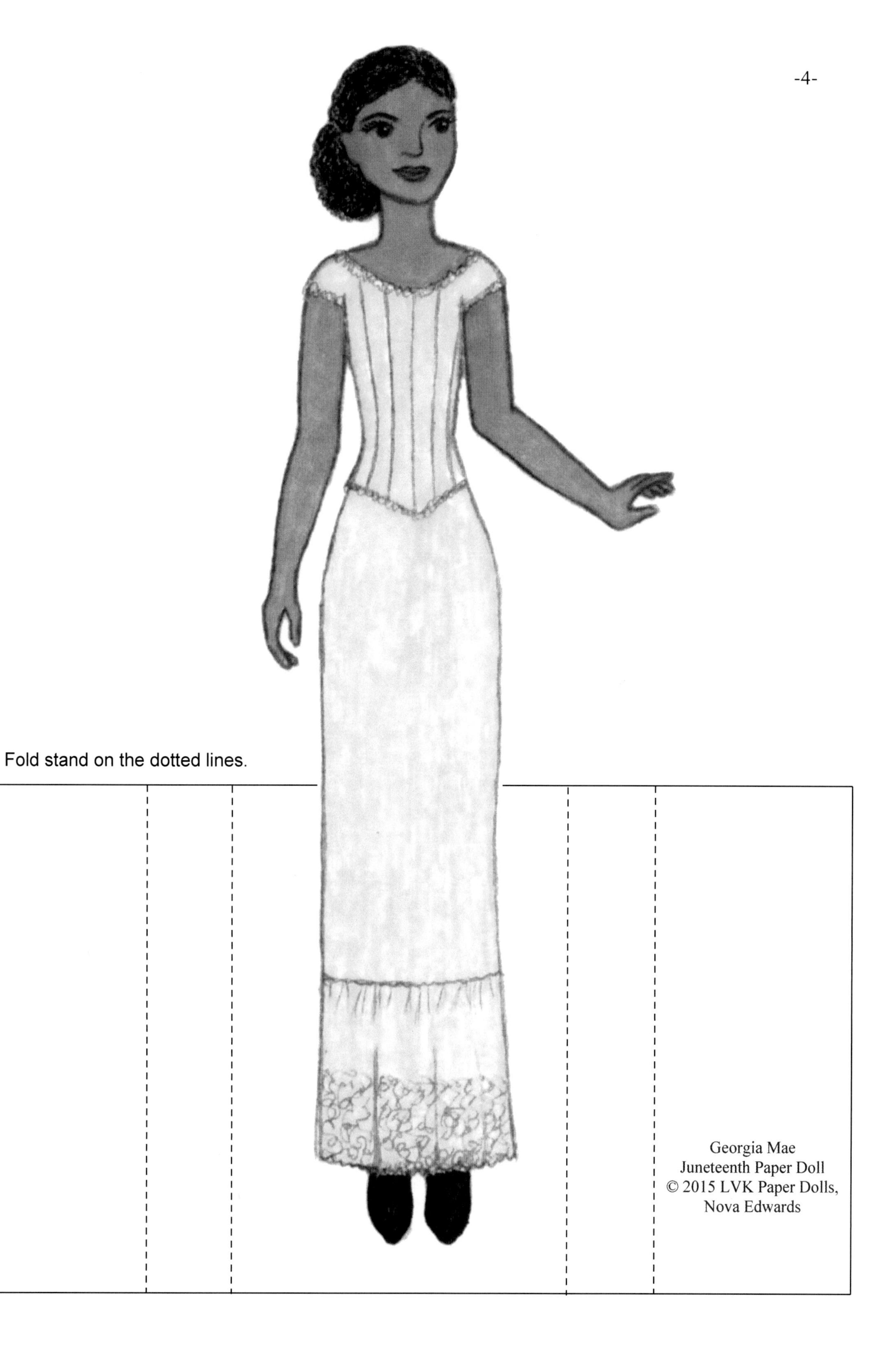
Fold stand on the dotted lines.
Georgia Mae
Juneteenth Paper Doll
© 2015 LVK Paper Dolls,
Nova Edwards

Juneteenth Paper Dolls


www.lvkpaperdolls.etsy.com

Juneteenth Paper Dolls



www.lvkpaperdolls.etsy.com

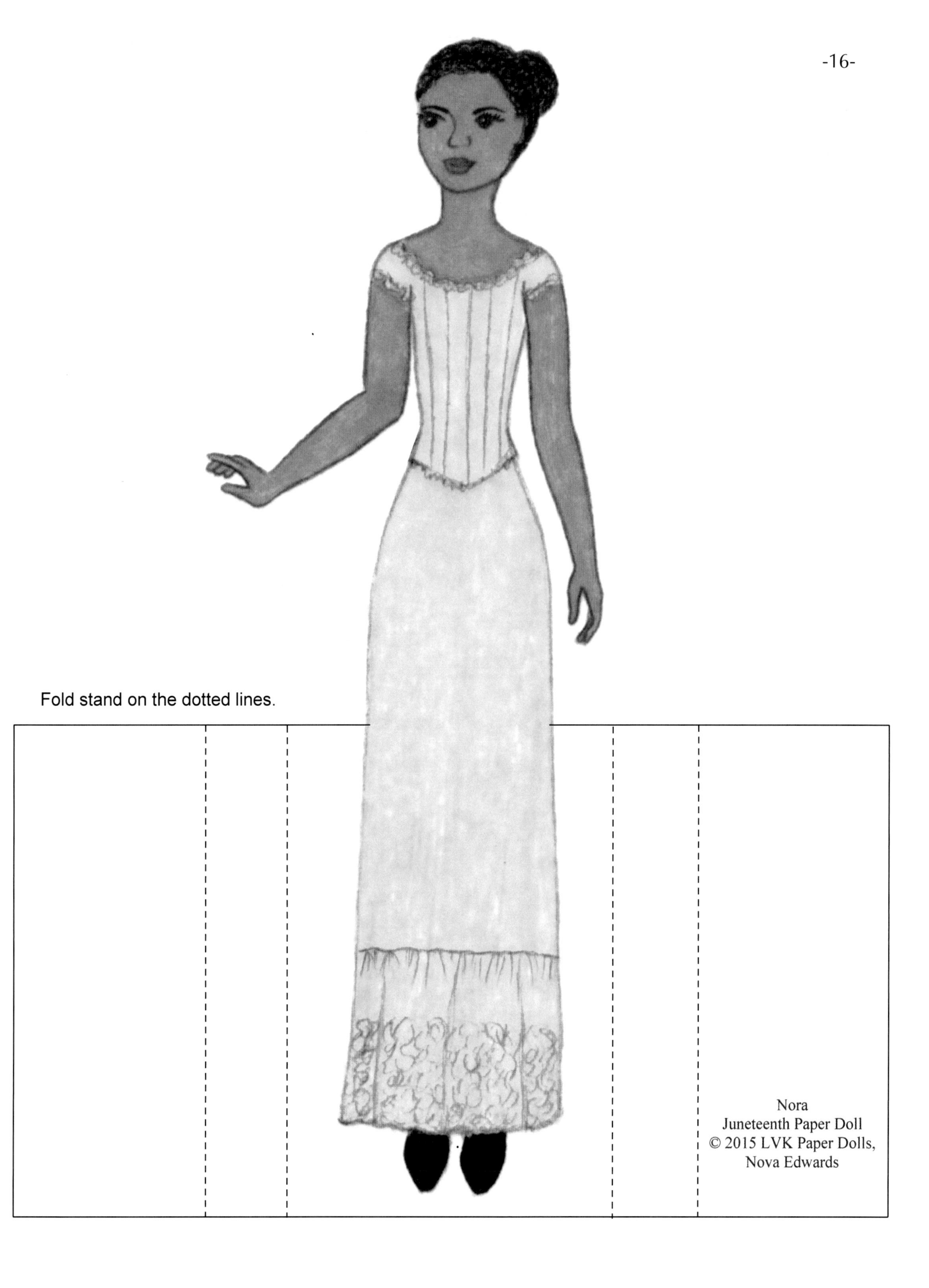
Fold stand on the dotted lines.
Nora
Juneteenth Paper Doll
© 2015 LVK Paper Dolls,
Nova Edwards

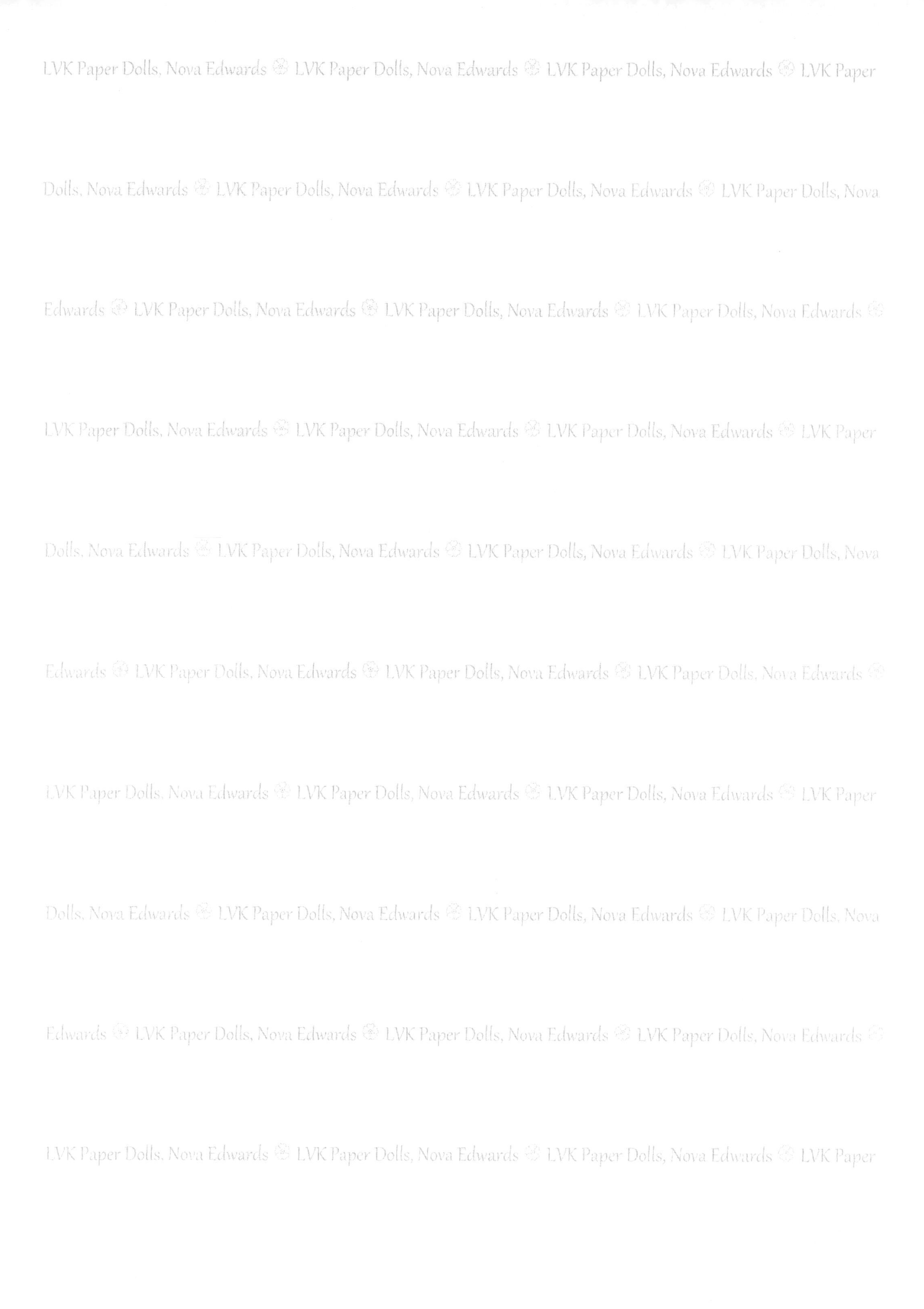
LVK Paper Dolls, Nova Edwards LVK Paper Dolls, Nova Edwards LVK Paper Dolls, Nova Edwards LVK Paper
Dolls, Nova Edwards LVK Paper Dolls, Nova Edwards LVK Paper Dolls, Nova Edwards LVK Paper Dolls, Nova
Edwards LVK Paper Dolls, Nova Edwards LVK Paper Dolls, Nova Edwards LVK Paper Dolls, Nova Edwards
LVK Paper Dolls, Nova Edwards LVK Paper Dolls, Nova Edwards LVK Paper Dolls, Nova Edwards LVK Paper
Dolls, Nova Edwards LVK Paper Dolls, Nova Edwards LVK Paper Dolls, Nova Edwards LVK Paper Dolls, Nova
Edwards LVK Paper Dolls, Nova Edwards LVK Paper Dolls, Nova Edwards LVK Paper Dolls, Nova Edwards
LVK Paper Dolls, Nova Edwards LVK Paper Dolls, Nova Edwards LVK Paper Dolls, Nova Edwards LVK Paper
Dolls, Nova Edwards LVK Paper Dolls, Nova Edwards LVK Paper Dolls, Nova Edwards LVK Paper Dolls, Nova
Edwards LVK Paper Dolls, Nova Edwards LVK Paper Dolls, Nova Edwards LVK Paper Dolls, Nova Edwards
LVK Paper Dolls, Nova Edwards LVK Paper Dolls, Nova Edwards LVK Paper Dolls, Nova Edwards LVK Paper

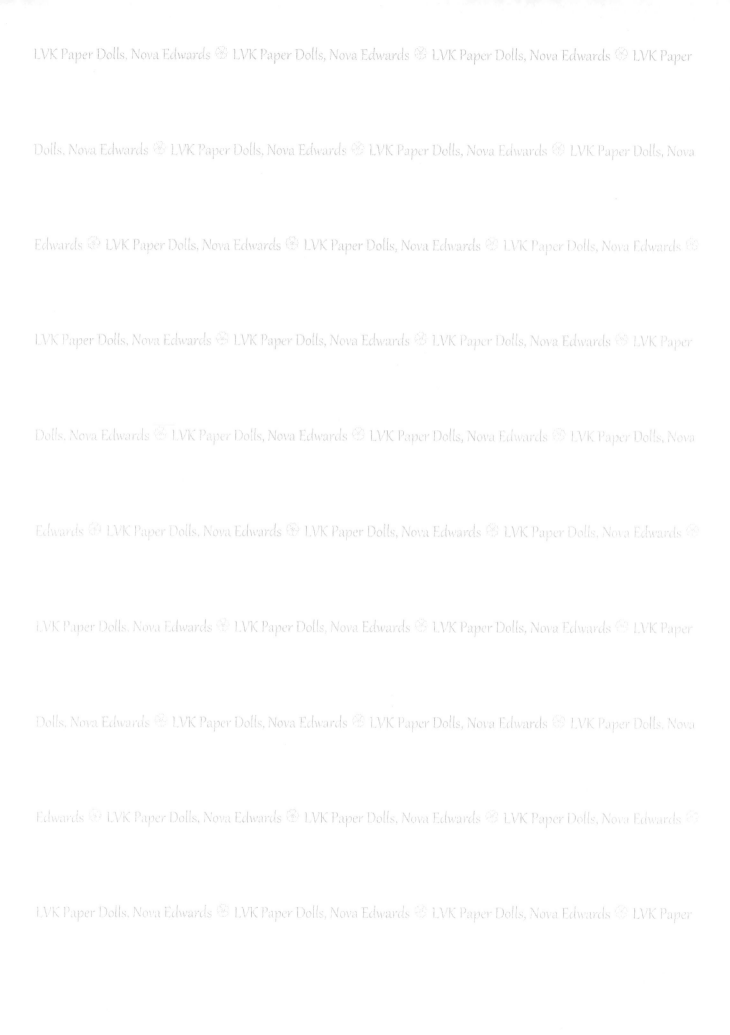

Cut on this line to remove the page.

Back of Envelope

Georgia Mae

Nora

# Juneteenth Paper Dolls

Commemorating the 150 Year Anniversary of the June 19, 1865
Announcement of the Abolishment of Slavery in the United States

Made in the USA
San Bernardino, CA
05 June 2020